Space Girl Sue

Written by Julia Donaldson
Illustrated by Clive Scruton

I saw a spacegirl.

Her name was Sue.

Her eyes were yellow, her hair was blue.

4

Her nose was green
and very long.

7

Her mouth was big.

Her arms were strong.

Her legs were pink.

Her hat was red.

She had a button on her head.

'Let's play,' I said.
'No, no,' said Sue.

She pressed her button

and off she flew.

I saw a spacegirl.
Her name was Sue.
Her eyes were yellow,
her hair was blue.
Her nose was green
and very long.
Her mouth was big.
Her arms were strong.
Her legs were pink.
Her hat was red.
She had a button
on her head.
'Let's play,' I said.
'No, no,' said Sue.
She pressed her button
and off she flew.